FISHWATCHERS' GUIDE

to
The Inshore Fishes of the Pacific Coast

by
Daniel W. Gotshall

SEA CHALLENGERS   •   MONTEREY, CALIFORNIA
1977

A Seachallengers Publication. Editorial consultation by The New Naturalist, a division of J. P. Harkins, Inc.

SEA CHALLENGERS
4 Sommerset Rise
Monterey, California 93940

LC   77-73915

First Edition

Printed in the United States of America

TABLE OF CONTENTS

FOREWORD

"Hey Fred, did you see the buck-toothed fish with the big bump on his forehead?"

"Yeah, I sure did Mike. And how about all those bright orange fish—weren't they sassy? Why one came right up and looked in my mask! I wonder what they are..."

One might overhear such a conversation just about any weekend of the year when some of the thousands of diving enthusiasts along North America's Pacific coast return to the beach after a dive. Most often the conversation would be carried on by a couple of neophyte divers who are just learning about the fascinating world underwater, but even the old salts run across a fish they've never seen before and are excited to find out what its name is.

Fishwatchers' Guide to the Inshore Fishes of the Pacific Coast was designed specifically for divers like Fred and Mike, as well as for the old salts. With this book Fred and Mike could have plopped themselves down on a rock and identified that buck-toothed fish as a Sheepshead and the bright orange fish as a Garibaldi.

Being able to identify fish in their natural habitats will open a whole new world of enjoyment for divers. Fish come in such different shapes and varieties of patterns and colors, have such different habits and, believe it or not, have such different personalities that it will be a joy to be able to look at the fish, then turn to this book with a full color picture of the fish, and a concise list of pertinent information about the species observed.

Divers won't be the only people to find this reference book invaluable—line fishermen, beachcombers and tidepool enthusiasts will be delighted with it. Even people sitting at home will enjoy the combined photographic expertise and knowledge of the marine environment displayed by the author, Dan Gotshall.

All along the Pacific coast, from Alaska to Baja California, there are hundreds of fascinating and beautiful fish to see and enjoy when you slip beneath the surface of the Pacific Ocean. This concise and accurate reference manual will surely help you to enjoy them...

Jack McKenney

INTRODUCTION

I present here a field guide to the common inshore fishes of the Pacific Coast from Southeastern Alaska to Baja California. This book is designed for the growing company of 'fishwatchers'— people who, through their interest in fishing, snorkeling, SCUBA diving, natural history or ecology, have come into contact with the fascinating and somewhat bewildering world of the fishes, and have sought to learn more about them. The key to this knowledge is identification. Once you know an animal's name, everything else begins to fall into place. Unfortunately, one soon learns that, for most parts of the world, there is little in the way of compact and accurate guides designed for non-specialists. On the Pacific Coast of North America, the last major work on the subject addressed to amateurs was the beautiful *Marine Game Fish of the Pacific Coast from Alaska to the Equator* by Lionel Walford, published by the Santa Barbara Museum of Natural History in 1937. Only 1500 copies of this work were ever printed and today it is a collector's item, commanding hundreds of dollars in the rare book market.

More than 600 species of fish have been reported off the Pacific Coast of North America. In setting the limits of this book, I set out to describe and picture those species most commonly observed by snorkelers and SCUBA divers in waters ranging from about 10 to about 150 feet. I have eliminated the well known game fish, the small fish that live in the turbid region near the shore and that tend to be difficult to identify, and fish that are extremely rare. I have also limited myself to species that can be identified alive in the water. For each species, I provide: nomenclature, range, depth, habitat, size, and distinguishing characteristics (field marks), and, for all but three, I give a full color photograph of a living specimen in its natural habitat.

To the best of my knowledge, the information presented here is the best and most recent available, but, since only a tiny fraction of the members of any species are ever taken for scientific observation, the reader must make allowance for error. This is especially true for range and depth information; the limits given here are simply those believed to be reported reliably. Unless otherwise specified, sizes given are the maximums reported to date, and the average adult will be somewhat smaller. Some of the information reported here is new and has never before been published. Such cases are indicated by a dagger in the text (†).

Nomenclature. For each species, I give the common name, the scientific name, and a translation of the scientific name. The common name is really the most common name—the name by which the species is known to sportsmen. These names are not standardized and are subject to some local variation. The scientific, or Latin names are standardized. They are the same throughout the world; the first word is the name of the genus to which the fish belongs, and the second is its specific name. Generally, a species is a group of freely interbreeding individuals, and a genus is a group of closely related species. Underneath the scientific names, I have provided translations of the Latin words and, occasionally, brief explanations. The symbol (↔) means that the translation is reversed; that is, the first term of the translation corresponds to the second term of the Latin.

How To Use This Book. For a fish that is totally unfamiliar, begin with the Key on Page 8. Using both the clues and the line drawings you will be able to narrow your specimen down to one or two families. The Key will direct you to the right part of the text. Examine the photographs carefully, and refer to the text. The best guide is usually habitat; fish found in kelp beds are unlikely to be found far away from them. Behavior is another good clue and so is range if you interpret it broadly enough. A species reported only as far south as Puget Sound is unlikely to appear off Point Conception. Field marks are usually reliable, but often you must get a good look, and you must know something about fish anatomy. The chart on the inside back cover will help you here.

New Information. As I have said, there is much that is not known about the fish of our region. In recent years, however, the increased popularity of salt water activities has been a real boon to the ichthyologist as a steady stream of new data and good leads has come in from interested amateurs. If you do come upon something that doesn't fit with the information in this book, I would very much like to know about it. Please address the author at: California Department of Fish and Game.

Monterey, California   Daniel W. Gotshall

ACKNOWLEDGEMENTS

Photographs of the bat ray, jack mackeral, salema, mola, and halfmoon were taken by the late Charles H. Turner. Jack Ames photographed the sargo, Daniel Miller produced the drawings of the whitspotted greenling, brown Irish lord and zebra goby, and John Fitch and Robert N. Lea provided identifications and information for several of the species. All are, or were, marine biologists with the California Department of Fish and Game. The red Irish lord and onespot fringehead were taken by Sea Library photographers Anne Harrington and Ken Lucas (Steinhart Aquarium); the starry flounder was also provided by Steinhart Aquarium photographer Ken Lucas; Rick Rosenthal photographed the rock greenling, and Tony Chess photographed the sharpnose surfperch and the Pacific electric ray.

Identifications and taxonomic information on some of the species also were provided by Robert Lavenberg, Curator of Fishes, Los Angeles County Museum of Natural History. Lillian Dempster, Curator of Fishes, California Academy of Sciences, translated several of the scientific names; information regarding species composition of the sport catch of Oregon skin and scuba divers was obtained from Jerry Butler, Oregon Fish Commission biologist. Line drawings are by Heidi H. Brunner, and the original manuscript was typed and edited by Ann Gotshall. Jerry Harkins was responsible for final editing; production and ultimate completion of this project.

To all of these people, and also to anyone I may have inadvertently overlooked, I owe a great debt of gratitude for making this book possible.

FAMILY KEY

A key is simply a series of choices. Each choice leads you either to another numbered choice or to the Family you are looking for. For example, Choice 1 leads you to either Choice 7 or Choice 2; Choice 2 leads to either Choice 3 or Choice 5; Choice 3 leads either to the Eaglerays on page 16, or to Choice 4; and so on.

1A Gill openings: (1) 7
 B Gill openings: (5 to 7) 2
2A Gill openings on underside of body 3
 B Gill openings on side of body 5

3A Dorsal fin: (1) or absent.
   Family Myliobatidiae
   (Eaglerays) ....(p. 16)
 B Dorsal fins: (2) 4

4A No spines or prickles on skin.
   Family Torpedinidae,
   (Electric rays) ....(p. 14)

 B Three rows of spines on tail.
   Family Platyrhinidae,
   (Thornbacks) ....(p. 16)

5A No anal fin. Family
   Squatinidae, (Angel
   Sharks) ....(p. 12)
 B Anal fin present 6
6A Spine in front of each dorsal
   fin. Family Heterodontidae,
   (Hornsharks)..............................(p. 12)
 B No spine in front of each
   dorsal fin and first dorsal
   fin above or behind pelvics.
   Family Scyliorhinidae,
   (Catsharks)...............................(p. 14)
7A Gill openings: (1) with eyes on same side of head 8
 B One eye on each side of head 9

8A Eyes usually on left side of
    head. Family Bothidae
    (Lefteyed flounders) . . . .(p. 98)

  B Eyes usually on right side of
    head. Family
    Pleuronectidae, (Righteyed
    flounders) . . . .(p. 100)
9A Pelvic fins absent 10
  B Pelvic fins present 13

10A No caudal fin; body deeply
    compressed. Family
    Molidae, (Molas) . . . .(p. 104)
  B Caudal fin present 11

11A Pectoral fins absent. Family
    Muraenidae, (Morays). . . . .(p. 18)
  B Pectoral fins present 12
12A Large doglike teeth, no dark
    bars below eye. Family
    Anarhichadidae, (Wolffishes). . . . . (p.88)
  B Teeth small, not doglike,
    two dark bars extending
    across cheek below eye.
    Family Cebidichthyidae,
    (Monkeyface-eels) . . . .(p. 94)
13A Pelvic fins thoracic; one spine and exactly five
    soft rays 14
  B Pelvic fins thoracic or jugular; less than five
    soft rays 26

14A Pelvic fins forming cone
    (i.e., united) Family
    Gobiidae, (Gobies) . . . .(p. 94)
  B Pelvic fins separated 15

15A Dorsal fin composed of
  soft rays only. Family
  Bathymasteridae,
  (Ronquils) . . . . (p. 86)
  B Dorsal fin with spines and soft rays 16
16A Suborbital stay present 17
  B Suborbital stay absent 19

17A Anal fin without spines.
  Family Cottidae,
  (Sculpins) . . . . (p. 50)
  B Anal fin with spines 18

18A Ridges and spines on head;
  4 to 11 soft anal rays. Family
  Scorpaenidae, (Rockfishes) . . . . (p. 20)
  B No ridges or spines on
  head; 12 or more soft anal
  rays. Family Hexagram-
  midae (Greenlings) . . . . (p. 46)
19A Lateral line terminates
  below posterior portion of
  dorsal fin. Family
  Pomacentridae,
  (Damsel fishes) . . . . (p. 80)
  B Lateral line extends at least to base of caudal fin 20
20A One or two anal spines.
  Family Branchiostegidae,
  (Tilefishes) . . . . (p. 64)
  B Three or four anal spines 21
21A Two anal spines isolated
  from fin. Family Carangidae,
  (Jacks) . . . . (p. 64)
  B Anal spines connected to soft rays 22
22A Sheath of scales extends
  out onto dorsal fin.
  Family Embiotocidae,
  (Surfperches) . . . . (p. 70)
  B No sheath of scales on dorsal fin 23

23A Maxillary mostly hidden by sliding under bone
above when mouth closed 24
 B Maxillary fully exposed
when mouth closed; three
spines on opercle. Family
Serranidae, (Sea basses) . . . . (p. 60)
24A Anterior teeth minute and
numerous, not canine-like
or incisor-like. Anal rays:
(10 or 11), lateral line
extends out onto caudal
rays. Family Pristipo-
matidae, (Grunts) . . . . (p. 66)
 B Anterior teeth either canine-like or incisor-like.
Lateral line does not extend out onto caudal rays.
Anal rays: (12 or more) 25

25A Anterior teeth canine-like.
Family Labridae, (Wrasses) . . . . (p. 82)

 B Anterior teeth incisor-like or
conical. Family Kyphosidae,
(Sea chubs) . . . . (p. 68)
26A Anal and dorsal fins
continuous with caudal fin.
Family Ophidiidae,
(Cusk eels) . . . . (p. 18)
 B Anal and dorsal fins separate from caudal fin 27
27A Dorsal fin preceded by
isolated spines. Family
Gasterosteidae (Tubesnouts
and Stickelbacks) . . . . (p. 20)
 B Dorsal fin not preceded by
isolated spines. Family
Clinidae (Clinids) . . . . (p. 88)

FAMILY HETERODONTIDAE
Horn Sharks

1. HORN SHARK   *Heterodontus francisci*
San Franciscan mixed-tooth (↔), so named because the original description was based on a specimen taken near the city.

Common around shallow, rocky reefs in Southern California; maximum recorded depth is 500 feet. These nocturnal sharks usually rest on the bottom during daylight, and are considered passive and easy to approach. May reach up to 4 feet. Identify by shape of head, body spots, and spines in front of each dorsal fin. Eggs laid in distinctive, grenade-shaped, horny case.

Recorded from Monterey, California to the Gulf of California, but not from Cape San Lucas, Baja California. Santa Catalina Island is center of abundance in this area.

FAMILY SQUATINIDAE
Angel Sharks

2. PACIFIC ANGEL   *Squatina californica*
   SHARKS   California skate (↔)

Angel sharks occur on the sandy bottom of inshore waters and bays, usually partially buried in sand. They reach up to 5 feet and 60 pounds. Look for skate-like body, gill slits in notch on sides behind head, and mouth at anterior edge of head. Angel sharks are easy to approach underwater, but have a nasty disposition if harassed. Bear live young.

Range is from Southeastern Alaska to the Gulf of California, but have not yet been recorded from British Columbia. Common around the Southern California Channel Islands.

1. HORN SHARK

2. PACIFIC ANGEL SHARK

FAMILY SCYLIORHINIDAE
Cat Sharks

3. SWELL SHARK *Cephaloscyllium ventriosum*
Pot-bellied head shark($\leftrightarrow$)

Although there are four members of this family in our area, only the swell shark occurs both in shallow water and in depths up to 1,380 feet. They are commonly found around shallow reefs in Southern California, particularly in caves and crevices. Length to at least 3⅓ feet. Look for mottling and spots on body. Swell sharks are the only members of the family that **do not** possess distinctive labial folds. These sharks are very sedentary, but will bite if harassed. Eggs laid in amber-colored cases.

Reported from Chile and Acapulco. Continuous known range is from Monterey Bay, California to Guadalupe Island, Baja California. Also common in upper Gulf of California.

FAMILY TORPEDINIDAE
Electric Rays

4. PACIFIC ELECTRIC RAY *Torpedo californica*
California electric ray ($\leftrightarrow$). The word, *torpedo*, which literally means *numbness,* was also used by the Romans to designate the Electric ray, presumably because of the effect the shock produces.

Occurs from shallow, inshore waters out to at least 640 feet, on sand or mud bottoms and occasionally around reefs. Sometimes pelagic. Maximum recorded size is 4 feet and 90 pounds. Look for a lead-gray color above and white underside. Body very flabby. No spines or prickles. These rays lack a venomous spine, but are capable of producing a strong electrical shock of up to 80 volts. They are very aggressive and divers have reported unprovoked attacks. Will enfold prey in fins to administer shock. Bear live young.

Range from Queen Charlotte Islands, British Columbia to Sebastian Viscaino Bay, Baja California.

3. SWELL SHARK

4. PACIFIC ELECTRIC RAY

FAMILY PLATYRHINIDAE
Thornbacks

5. THORNBACK *Platyrhinoidis triseriata*
Broad snout; three rows

These rays are common on sandy bottoms in Southern California, to a maximum recorded depth of 150 feet. Length to 2½ feet, weight to 5¾ pounds. Look for 2 dorsal fins, and the 3 rows of prominent spines on posterior dorsal surface that give the specific name.

Range from San Francisco to Thurloe Head, Baja California.

FAMILY MYLIOBATIDIDAE
Eagle Rays

6. BAT RAY *Myliobatis californica*
California grinder ray (↔). The name "grinder" comes from the flat grinding teeth used to crush clams and oysters.

Common in shallow bays. Occasionally found around reefs out to 150 feet. Maximum recorded size is 4 feet in width and 210 pounds; however, recent observations off Southern California indicate larger specimens may exist. Sometimes occur in schools or aggregations. Look for head and eyes projecting forward of origin of pectoral fin, and single dorsal fin. Considered a major predator by oystermen. Also prey on abalone, particularly in Southern California. Bear live young. Beware of venomous spine on tail.

Range from Oregon to the Gulf of California.

5. THORNBACK

6. BAT RAY

FAMILY MURAENIDAE
Moray Eels

7. CALIFORNIA MORAY *Gymnothorax mordax*
naked breast; biting. Morays have a habit of holding the mouth open for short periods as if threatening to bite, but this behavior is actually related to the movement of water through the gill system.

Occurs in rocky areas from shallow water to about 130 feet[†], sometimes in same crevices as lobsters. Usually remain hidden in holes and caves during daytime and come out to feed at night. Length to 5 feet. No pectoral or pelvic fins. Is a major predator on octopus.

Reported from Point Conception south to Magdalena Bay, Baja California.

FAMILY OPHIDIIDAE
Cusk-eels

8. SPOTTED CUSK-EEL *Otophidium taylori*
Taylor's ear-snake (↔), after A.S. Taylor, discoverer of this species.

Found on sand and mud bottoms in water 4 to 800 feet deep. Length to 14¼ inches. Look for chin whiskers and dark spots on back and sides. Noted for its ability to burrow into the sand tail first. It is unusual to see them during daytime except in early morning and late afternoon and in dirty water. At night, they venture from their hiding places in the sand to feed on small fish, octopus, and crustaceans.

Northern Oregon to San Cristobal Bay, Baja California.

7. CALIFORNIA MORAY

8. SPOTTED CUSK-EEL

FAMILY GASTEROSTEIDAE
Tubesnouts

9. TUBESNOUT *Aulorhynchus flavidus*
(tube snout) (yellow)

Common in kelp beds, particularly in midwater and surface part of canopy; also occurs in eelgrass beds in bays. Maximum depth reported, 100 feet. Length to 7 inches. Look for long snout and 23 to 26 isolated spines in front of dorsal fin. Tubesnouts, like their close relative, the stickleback (*Gasterosteus sp.*) are nest builders. The nests are constructed and defended by the males. Sitka, Alaska to Pt. Rompiente, Baja California.

FAMILY SCORPAENIDAE
Rockfish

Note: This family contains more members than any other found in the temperate waters of the Eastern Pacific. There are 4 genera in our area, but we will treat only the 2 which are common in shallow water. All members of the genus *Sebastes* bear life young in the form of very small larvae which float in the upper water layers as part of the plankton for the first few weeks of their lives.

10. BOCACCIO *Sebastes paucispinis*
magnificent; few spines

Juveniles found around shallow, inshore reefs and piers; adults range out to a depth of 1050 feet. Maximum size said to be 36 inches. Similar to chilipepper (*Sebastes goodei,* not included here) but look for large mouth and darker back of bocaccio, the maxillary extending to behind the eye.

Reported from Kruzof Island, Alaska to Punta Blanca, Baja California, with center of abundance between Fort Bragg and Santa Barbara, California.

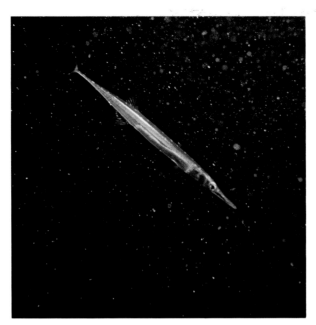

9. TUBESNOUT

JUVENILE   ADULT

10. BOCACCIO

11. BLACK ROCKFISH   *Sebastes melanops*
magnificent; black face

Juveniles found in tide pools; adults have been taken as deep as 360 feet around reefs and over sand and mud bottoms. One of the most common shallow water rockfishes found off Northern California, Oregon, and Washington. Maximum recorded length is 23¾ inches. Similar to the blue rockfish (No. 12), but look for the longer maxillary that extends beneath the rear of the eye, a rounded anal fin, dark spots on the adult dorsal fin, and light gray lateral line. Where both species are seen together, the black will be seen to have a much larger eye.

Recorded from Amchitka Island, Alaska to Paradise Cove, California.

12. BLUE ROCKFISH   *Sebastes mystinus*
magnificent; priest

Very abundant in depths of 100 feet or less around reefs and kelp beds; have been caught as deep as 300 feet off California and, reportedly, as deep as 1200 feet off Southeastern Alaska. May reach 21 inches but most are smaller than 16 inches. Similar to black rockfish (No. 11), but look for shorter maxillary that does not extend beyond mid-eye, and the straight posterior profile of the anal fin. Also, the blue rockfish has no spots on dorsal fin, and does not have the light gray lateral line of the black rockfish. Blue rockfish usually occur in large schools or aggregations.

Found from the Bering Sea to Santo Tomas, Baja California. Most abundant from Fort Bragg to Point Conception, California.

11. BLACK ROCKFISH

12. BLUE ROCKFISH

13. WIDOW ROCKFISH

Sebastes entomelas
(magnificent) (within black)

Adults occur in large schools or aggregations around offshore reefs from near surface to 1050 feet. Juveniles frequent shallow waters. Common around oil towers off Southern California. Length to 21 inches. Look for black membranes in anal, pectoral and pelvic fins and maxillary not reaching beyond middle of eye. Primarily a plankton feeder. Of minor importance in sport and commercial fisheries.

Southern Alaska to Todos Santos Bay, Baja California.

14. YELLOWTAIL ROCKFISH

Sebastes flavidus
magnificent; yellow

Juveniles found in tide pools and around inshore reefs and kelp beds. Adults have been caught as deep as 600 feet. Large schools are common at mid-depth over reefs. Length to 26 inches. Often confused with olive rockfish (No. 15). Look for two distinctive yellow areas on gill covers, light orange-brown speckles on body scales, and 8 rays in anal fin. Recent studies in Alaska suggest that yellowtails have a homing instinct.

Range from Forrester Island, Southeastern Alaska to San Diego.

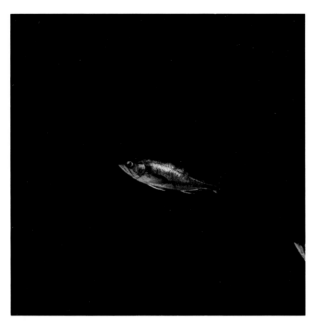

13. WIDOW ROCKFISH

14. YELLOWTAIL ROCKFISH

15. OLIVE ROCKFISH

Sebastes serranoides
magnificent; resembling the Serranidae, or Sea-Bass Family.

Found singly and in schools around shallow kelp beds and reefs to depths of 480 feet. Juveniles are common in tidepools. Maximum recorded length is 24 inches. Look for 9 or more soft rays in the anal fin. Similar to yellowtail rockfish (No. 14), but the olive does not have the yellow blotches on gill covers, or the orange brown speckles on the body scales. Found most often off the bottom.

From Redding Rock, California to the San Benito Islands, Baja California. Center of abundance is from Monterey south.

16. VERMILION ROCKFISH

Sebastes miniatus
magnificent vermilion

Adults may be observed or caught near the bottom around reefs and occasionally over sand or mud bottoms in depths from 60 to 660 feet. Juveniles sometimes found in water as shallow as 20 to 30 feet. Length to at least 30 inches. Look for rough scales on underside of jaw and on maxillary. The yelloweye (No. 18) and canary (No. 17) rockfish, which closely resemble the vermilion, do not have these scales. Non-schooling. These fish are highly desired by sport fishermen for food.

Vancouver Island to San Benito Islands, Baja California.

15. OLIVE ROCKFISH

16. VERMILION ROCKFISH

17. CANARY ROCKFISH *Sebastes pinniger*
magnificent; large-finned

Juveniles can be observed around reefs from 30 to 60 feet, but mature adults are seldom found in waters less than 80 feet deep. Maximum known depth is 660 feet. Adults frequent sand and mud bottoms as well as reefs. Maximum recorded size is 30 inches. Look for large black spot on spinous dorsal fin in specimens up to 14 inches, and yellow-orange and gray body coloration. Underside of jaw and maxillary lack rough scales. A very important commercial species.

Reported from Cape Bartolome, Southeastern Alaska to Cape Colnett, Baja California.

18. YELLOWEYE ROCKFISH *Sebastes ruberrimus*
magnificent, very red

Juveniles found as shallow as 60 feet, adults from 80[†] to 1200 feet. Both prefer rocky reefs with large crevices and caves. Length reported to 36 inches. Look for yellow eye and flattened rasp-like spines on the head of adults. Juveniles have 2 silvery-white stripes on sides. No scales under jaw or on maxillary. Highly esteemed food fish.

Gulf of Alaska to Ensenada, Baja California.

17. CANARY ROCKFISH

JUVENILE   ADULT

18. YELLOWEYE ROCKFISH

19. KELP ROCKFISH

Sebastes atrovirens
magnificent; black-green

Common around kelp beds and reefs to 150 feet. Largest specimen was 16¾ inches. Easily confused with the grass rockfish (No. 20) but gill rakers on first gill arch are long and slender, not short and stubby. Commonly found in kelp forest off the bottom drifting sometimes head up, sometimes head down, thus the nickname "dumb bass."

Inshore waters from Timber Cove, California to San Benito Islands, Baja California

20. GRASS ROCKFISH

Sebastes rastrelliger
magnificent; rake bearing, referring to gill rakers.

Common from Central California south in intertidal and shallow subtidal rocky kelp beds, out to about 50 feet. Length to 22 inches. Look for a thick caudal peduncle, dark olive green mottling, and 22-25 short stubby gill rakers on the first gill arch. The grass rockfish is the only member of this family with this type of gill raker. They are very cryptic, living in holes and crevices. Best time to observe them is at night when they come out to forage.

Yaquina Bay, Oregon south to Playa Maria Bay, Baja California.

19. KELP ROCKFISH

20. GRASS ROCKFISH

21. BROWN ROCKFISH   *Sebastes auriculatus*
magnificent; eared

Commonly found on or near the bottom around low profile shale or sandstone reefs out to about 200. Usually found on bottom, but seldom in kelp beds or water of high visibility. Length to 21½ inches. Look for dark brown to black spot on gill cover, and coronal spine.

Southeastern Alaska to Hipolito Bay, Baja Caliornia.

22. QUILLBACK   *Sebastes maliger*
ROCKFISH   magnificent; mast-bearing

Common around rocky areas as shallow as 35 feet[†] in Southeastern Alaska and British Columbia. Often in caves and crevices. Maximum reported depth is 900 feet. Length to 24 inches. Look for deeply incised membranes of spinous dorsal fin, and brown spots on anterior ventral portion of body. Non-schooling.

Prince William Sound, Alaska to Point Sur, California.

21. BROWN ROCKFISH

22. QUILLBACK ROCKFISH

23. CHINA ROCKFISH *Sebastes nebulosus*
magnificent; clouded

These distinctive fish occur in and around rocky reefs, the young in water as shallow as 10[†], adults to depths of 420 feet. Maximum recorded length is 17 inches. Look for a bright yellow stripe extending from anterior dorsal fin to lateral line and then rearward toward tail. Also, yellow or whitish spots on anterior portion of body. These solitary and cryptic rockfish from a minor portion of the sport and commercial catch.

Southeastern Alaska to San Miguel Island, California.

24. BLACK-AND-YELLOW *Sebastes chrysomelas*
ROCKFISH magnificent; gold-black

Found around rocky reefs and kelp beds in depths from 10 to 120 feet. Length to 16⅓ inches. Indistinguishable from gopher rockfish (No. 25) except for color. Look for yellow blotches on black body. Also, as a general rule, the black-and-yellow will be in shallower water than the gopher.

Eureka, California to Punta San Carlos, Baja California.

23. CHINA ROCKFISH

24. BLACK-AND-YELLOW ROCKFISH

25. GOPHER ROCKFISH   *Sebastes carnatus*
magnificent; flesh-colored

Found around rocky reefs in depths from 10 to 180 feet. Length to 15½ inches. Look for large, whitish to flesh-colored spots between lateral line and dorsal fin, and dark brown body. Common, easily approached, non-schooling rockfish.

Reported from Eureka, California to San Roque, Baja California. Uncommon north of Shelter Cove, California.

26. COPPER ROCKFISH   *Sebastes caurinus*
magnificent; and northwestern

Found around inshore reefs out to 60 feet, uncommon beyond 150 feet. Length to 22½ inches. Often confused with brown rockfish (No. 21) but the copper lacks coronal spines. Also look for clear area along the posterior two-thirds of the lateral line. Some taxonomists believe that the copper rockfish is really the same species as the whitebelly rockfish (*S. vexillaris*) which is not included here.

Known range for both species is Kenai Penninsula, Alaska to San Benito Islands, Baja California.

25. GOPHER ROCKFISH

26. COPPER ROCKFISH

27. CALICO ROCKFISH   *Sebastes dalli*

magnificent; of Dall, after W. H. Dall, naturalist.

Usually found around rocky reefs but occasionally over sand in depths from 60 to 840 feet. Length to 10 inches. Look for yellow-green body marked with irregular, brown bars and blotches. Generally in association with honeycomb (No. 28), starry (No. 30), and rosy (No. 29) rockfish.

San Francisco to Rompiente, Baja California.

28. HONEYCOMB ROCKFISH   *Sebastes umbrosus*

magnificent; shady

Found around rocky reefs and occasionally over sand in depths from 80[†] to 250 feet. Length to 10½ inches. Look for blackish margins on scales forming a honeycomb pattern, and 3 to 5 white blotches on back. Honeycomb rockfish are similar to freckled rockfish (*Sebastes lentiginosus*, not included) but they lack toothed knobs on the premaxillaries.

Point Pinos, California to Punta San Juanico, Baja California.

27. CALICO ROCKFISH

28. HONEYCOMB ROCKFISH

29. ROSY ROCKFISH   *Sebastes rosaceus*
magnificent; rosy

These bright red rockfish have been observed around rocky reefs as shallow as 50 feet, and have been taken from water as deep as 420 feet. Maximum recorded length is slightly more than 14 inches. Look for white blotches with purplish-red borders on back. This small fish is considered one of the finest eating of the rockfish.

Reported from Queen Charlotte Sound, British Columbia to Turtle Bay, Baja California.

30. STARRY ROCKFISH   *Sebastes constellatus*
magnificent; starry

Occurs around rocky reefs in depths from 65† to 540 feet. Length to 18 inches. Look for the 5 whitish blotches between lateral line and dorsal fin, and the small white spots that cover the body. Starry rockfish are easily approached by divers. Non-schooling. Usually remains close to crevices where it seeks shelter when threatened.

San Francisco to Thetis Bank, Baja California.

29. ROSY ROCKFISH

30. STARRY ROCKFISH

31. TREEFISH   *Sebastes serriceps*
magnificant; saw-head

Found in depths from 10 to 150 feet around rocky reefs. Length to 16 inches. Look for olive-yellow body with black bars, red lips. Hovers upside down or vertically on cave ceilings.

San Francisco to Cedros Island, Baja California.

32. TIGER ROCKFISH   *Sebastes nigrocinctus*
magnificent; black belt

This very cryptic rockfish occurs in and around rocky reefs that contain caves and crevices, in depths from 100[†] to 900 feet. Length to 24 inches. Look for a light orange to pink body marked with vertical black to reddish black bars. Reportedly changes color to a darker shade when disturbed. A solitary rockfish, very aggressive in protecting its territory.

Southeastern Alaska to Point Buchon, California.

31. TREEFISH

32. TIGER ROCKFISH

33. PUGET SOUND ROCKFISH

Sebastes emphaeus
(Magnificent) (display)

Fairly common around rocky areas as shallow as 35 feet. Maximum recorded length is 7 inches. Look for greenish-brown bars and blotches on a copper-red body. These colors tend to appear faded underwater. Females release young during August and September.

Recorded only from the protected waters of Puget Sound, San Juan Islands and near Lion's Bay, British Columbia.

34. SCULPIN

Scorpaena guttata
dorsal spines; speckled

Occurs intertidally out to 600 feet on rocky reefs and sometimes on sand. Most abundant in depths less than 100 feet. Length to 17 inches. These fish do not bear live young. Instead, they lay eggs embedded in transparent, pear-shaped cases. The eggs are released on the bottom and then rise to the surface where they hatch in about 5 days. Look for 8-10 soft rays in dorsal fin and note absence of teeth on palatine bone. Sculpin should be handled with extreme care as the dorsal, anal, and pelvic spines are venomous.

Santa Cruz, California into the Gulf of California.

33. PUGET SOUND ROCKFISH

34. SCULPIN

FAMILY HEXAGRAMMIDAE
Greenlings

Note: We include here five species in three genera. All are very edible, but only lingcod occur in large enough numbers to be considered commercially important.

35. KELP GREENLING   *Hexagrammos decagrammus*
six-line; ten-line

Juveniles found in shallow bays on sand and mud bottoms, and in the rocky intertidal. Adults inhabit reefs to depths of 150 feet. Length to 21 inches, but averages from 12 to 16 inches. Look for two pairs of cirri, one over the eyes and the other between the eye and the origin of the dorsal fin. Occasionally the second pair is absent. Cirri over eye never more than ¾ the diameter of the eye. 5 lateral lines. Yellowish mouth interior. Males and females differ in coloration, an example of sexual dimorphism (see photographs). One of the most common inshore non-schooling fishes from central California.

Aleutian Islands, Alaska to La Jolla, California.

36. WHITESPOTTED GREENLING   *Hexagrammos stelleri*
six-line; of Steller, for G. W. Steller, 18th Century German naturalist who accompanied Bering to Alaska in 1741.

Found in shallow rocky areas, as well as on sand. Reportedly reaches 19 inches. Look for white spots on body, a very slender caudal peduncle, and a short 4th lateral line that does not extend beyond origin of anal fin.

In Eastern Pacific range, from the Bering Sea to Coos Bay, Oregon[†].

Male   Female

35. KELP GREENLING

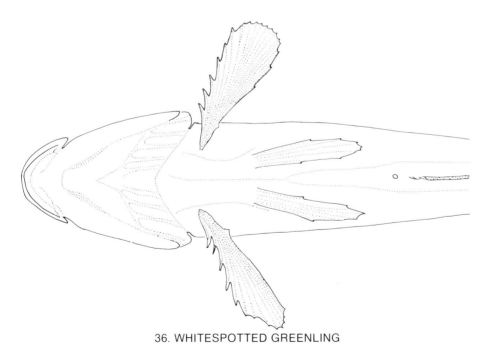

36. WHITESPOTTED GREENLING

37. ROCK GREENLING   *Hexagrammos superciliosus*
six-line; large cirri

Found near intertidal rocky reefs and kelp beds to depths of about 50 feet. Reportedly reaches 24 inches. Look for blue mouth and large cirri over eye. Cirri will be more than ¾ diameter of eye. Color is extremely variable; as far as known, males and females do not differ in color pattern.

Bering Sea to Point Conception, California.

38. LINGCOD   *Ophiodon elongatus*
snake tooth; elongated

Found around rocky reefs; juveniles occasionally on sand or mud bottoms. Intertidal region to depths of 1400 feet. Length to 60 inches; weight to 100 pounds. Except for salmon, probably most popular ocean sport fish from Northern California to Washington.

Kodiak Island, Alaska to Point San Carlos, Baja California.

37. ROCK GREENLING

38. LINGCOD

39. PAINTED GREENLING *Oxylebius pictus*

Painted sharp lebius (↔). "Lebius" is another name for "hexagrammos."

Found around rocky reefs, intertidally out to depths of 160 feet. Length to 10 inches. This non-schooling fish is commonly observed by skin and SCUBA divers, but is rarely taken by hook-and-line fishermen, probably because of the small mouth. Males and females colored differently.

Queen Charlotte Islands, British Columbia south to Point San Carlos, Baja California.

FAMILY COTTIDAE
Sculpins

Note: This large family contains at least 56 species which are found in our area. Most are small, difficult to identify, shallow water fish rarely encountered by fishermen. We have included here 10 species that can be recognized and that are commonly encountered by divers and fishermen.

40. CABEZON

Scorpaenichthys marmoratus
dorsal spined fish; marbled. Genus named after the Sculpin (No. 34).

Occurs intertidally out to depths of 250 feet around rocky reefs and in kelp beds. Maximum reported length is 39 inches, but this not verified. Look for lack of scales on body, and a single cirrus on snout. A very popular sport fish, although it does not occur in large numbers. Considered a major abalone predator.

Sitka, Alaska to Point Abreojos, Baja California.

39. PAINTED GREENLING

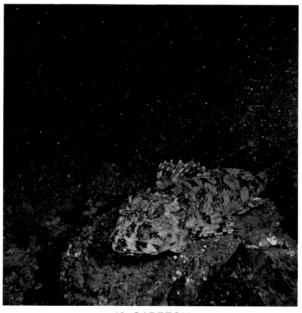

40. CABEZON

41. GREAT SCULPIN   *Myoxocephalus polyacanthocephalus*
(dormouse head) (many head spine)

Common on sandy and rocky bottoms as shallow as 5 feet. There are at least three species of *Myoxocephalus* reported from the Gulf of Alaska and Southeastern Alaska. The great sculpin, apparently the largest of this genera, reaches a maximum length of 30 inches. Look for long, straight, smooth upper operculer spine, and scales embedded in fleshy papillae on head.

Reported from Washington north to Bering Sea and then south to Japan.

42. LONGFIN SCULPIN   *Jordania zonope*
Jordan; zone-window. Genus named after David Starr Jordan, ichthyologist.

Occurs on rocky substrate intertidally out to depths of 126 feet. Length to 5-1/10 inches. Look for 3 black vertical bars below eye and 17-18 spines in dorsal fin. Considered rare before advent of SCUBA. Divers often see these fish upside down near crevice openings or on vertical rock faces.

Barkley Sound, British Columbia to Diablo Canyon, California.

41. GREAT SCULPIN

42. LONGFIN SCULPIN

43. BROWN IRISH LORD *Hemilepidotus spinosus*
half-scaled; spiny

Frequents rocky areas, intertidally to 252 feet. Length to 10 inches. Look for 7-8 scale rows between lateral line and dorsal fin. Brown Irish lords are very difficult to distinguish from red Irish lords (No. 44) underwater. Generally, the browns are predominantly brown with only a few patches of red, while the reds always have some red markings on the upper part of the body.

Puffin Island, Southeastern Alaska to Santa Barbara, California.

44. RED IRISH LORD *Hemilepidotus hemilepidotus*
half-scaled; half-scaled

Found on rocky reefs, intertidally out to depths of 156 feet. Length to 20 inches. Look for 4 or 5 rows of scales under dorsal fin. Most divers probably swim right by the red Irish lord because its coloration usually blends with the plants and animals in its vicinity. Occasionally caught by hook-and-line fishermen.

Sea of Okhotsk to Monterey Bay.

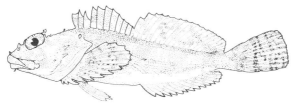

43. BROWN IRISH LORD

44. RED IRISH LORD

45. SAILFIN SCULPIN *Nautichthys oculofasciatus*
sailor fish; eye-banded

Occurs on rocky reefs and occasionally on sand and mud bottoms, intertidally out to 360 feet. Length to 6⅘ inches. Look for high, spiny dorsal fin and a dark vertical band running through eye. These distinctive fish are best observed by divers at night when they come out to forage.

Reported from Eastern Kamchatka to San Miguel Island, California.

46. GRUNT SCULPIN *Rhamphocottus richardsonii*
Snout cottid; Richardson's after John Richardson, naturalist.

Found on rocky substrate, sometimes on sandy bottom, intertidally to 540 feet. Reaches 3⅓ inches. Look for distinctive elongated snout on a head that is half the length of the fish. Pectoral fins lower rays free—that is, without connective membrane. Grunt sculpin are fairly commonly observed by divers in Puget Sound and British Columbia. They make excellent aquarium fish due to their interesting behavior.

Bering Sea to Santa Monica Bay, California.

45. SAILFIN SCULPIN

46. GRUNT SCULPIN

47. BUFFALO SCULPIN *Enophrys bison*
on eyebrow; buffalo

A common inhabitant of rocky intertidal and shallow subtidal areas. Occasionally found on sand. Length to slightly more than 14½ inches. Look for the long, preopercular spine and bony plates on lateral line. Often caught by hook-and-line fishermen, but not esteemed as a food fish.

Kodiak Island to Monterey, California.

48. SNUBNOSE SCULPIN *Orthonopias triacis*
straight eyes; three points

Occurs on rocky reefs, intertidally to depths of 100 feet. Length to 4 inches. Look for snub nose and anus located nearer to pelvic origin than to origin of anal fin.

Monterey to San Geronimo Island, Baja California.

47. BUFFALO SCULPIN

48. SNUBNOSE SCULPIN

49. LAVENDER SCULPIN *Leiocottus hirundo*

Smooth cottid; swallow. The "smooth" refers to the lack of visible scales.

On sandy bottoms, occasionally on rocks, intertidally to 120 feet. Length to 10 inches. Look for distinctive coloration and a long first and second dorsal spine. A common, medium size sculpin of shallow Southern California waters. Considered rare before advent of SCUBA.

Goleta, California[†] to Point Banda, Baja California.

FAMILY SERRANIDAE
Sea Basses

Ten members of this family have been reported from this area. Most of these, however, are uncommon north of Baja California. Included here are descriptions of three common species.

50. KELP BASS *Paralabrax clathratus*

related to *Labrax;* latticed. Genus name refers to another genus of Sea Bass.

Common in Southern California around kelp beds from surface to depths of 150 feet. The largest specimen on record was 28⅖ inches and 14½ pounds. Look for the 3rd dorsal fin spine, which is about the same length as the fourth and fifth spine, and whitish blotches between lateral line and base of dorsal fin. A very popular sport fish in Southern California. Old fish have dusky, orange-yellow chins.

Columbia River to Magdalena Bay, Baja California.

49. LAVENDER SCULPIN

50. KELP BASS

51. SPOTTED SAND BASS
Paralabrax maculatofasiatus
related to *Labrax;* spotted-banded

Occurs around reefs and on sand in shallow water. Maximum recorded depth is 200 feet. Length to 22 inches. Look for black spots on body. 3rd dorsal fin spine is longer than 4th or 5th spines. Dusky bars on sides covered with spots. Divers frequently encounter spotted sand bass, but hook-and-line fishermen do not take them often enough for them to be considered important game fish.

Monterey, California to Mazatlan, Mexico.

52. BARRED SAND BASS
Paralabrax nebulifer
related to *Labrax;* cloud-bearing

Occurs on sand and shale reef bottoms from shallow water to a reported depth of 600 feet. Maximum length is 25⅗ inches. Look for dusky bars on side, and longer 3rd dorsal fin spine. Similar to spotted sand bass (No. 51) but **without** black spots on body. The barred sand bass is an important component of the catch of southern California party boat fishermen.

From Santa Cruz, California to Magdalena Bay, Baja California.

51. SPOTTED SAND BASS

52. BARRED SAND BASS

FAMILY BRANCHIOSTEGIDAE
Tilefish

53. OCEAN WHITEFISH *Caulolatilus princeps*
distinguished from *Latilus;* leader.
Latilus is a closely related genus having
fewer fin rays.

Occurs around reefs and kelp beds and over sand bottoms from shallow water out to 300 feet. Length to 40 inches. Look for the long dorsal fin which is of constant height throughout its length. This is a fine sportfish which many people tend to underrate.

Reported from Vancouver Island British Columbia to Peru.

FAMILY CARANGIDAE
Jacks

Note: Thirteen species of jacks have been reported from our area, but only two range north of California. These are pelagic fish and the larger species are considered prime sport fish. The yellowtail, (*Seriola dorsalis*), not described here, is one of the most sought-after game species in Southern California. Included here is the single species most often encountered by divers.

54. JACK MACKEREL *Trachurus symmetricus*
rough tail; symmetrical

Frequents upper water layers, but is commonly observed in large schools around reefs and kelp beds. Maximum reported depth is 150 feet. Length to 32 inches. Look for enlarged lateral line scales that form sharp ridges on each side of tail. Accessory lateral line and anterior lateral line scales same size as posterior lateral line scales. A popular sport and commercial fish in Southern California. The record commercial catch was 146 million pounds for the year 1952.

Southeastern Alaska to Magdalena Bay, Baja California.

53. OCEAN WHITEFISH

54. JACK MACKEREL

FAMILY PRISTIPOMATIDAE
Grunts

55. SARGO   *Anisotremus davidsonii*
unequal aperture; Davidson's, after George Davidson, astronomer of the California Academy of Sciences.

Occurs in shallow water around kelp beds and rocky reefs associated with sand, out to depths of 130 feet. Length to 17 2/5 inches and weight to 3 7/10 pounds. Look for black vertical bar on adults that extends from middle of spiny dorsal fin down to level of pectoral fin. These fish are common in Southern California and usually occur in small schools. Introduced into the Salton Sea in 1951 and is now one of the most numerous species caught there by sport fishermen.

Santa Cruz, California to Magdalena Bay, Baja California.

56. SALEMA   *Xenistius californiensis*
strange sail; California

Common in shallow water south of Santa Barbara. Maximum · length to 10 inches. Look for large eye, separate spiny and soft-ray dorsal fins, and 6-8 horizontal orange-brown stripes on sides. Usually observed in large schools off bottom.

Monterey Bay, California to Peru.

55. SARGO

56. SALEMA

FAMILY KYPHOSIDAE
Sea Chubs

57. OPALEYE   *Girella nigricans*
small wrasse; blackfish

Juveniles found in tidepools; adults have been caught as deep as 95 feet around reefs and kelp beds. Length to 25 2/5 inches and weight to 12½ pounds. Look for 1-2 whitish spots on back, blue opalescent eye, and blue-green body color. Opaleyes are common in Southern California, forming loose schools and aggregations although divers find them difficult to approach. Mostly sought by shore fishermen.

San Francisco to Cape San Lucas, Baja California.

58. HALFMOON   *Medialuna californiensis*
California half-moon (↔)

Occurs in kelp beds and around reefs from the surface to 130 foot depths. Maximum length to 19 inches and weight to 4 pounds. Look for distinctive half-moon shape of tail, overall gray-blue body color, and sheath of scales covering soft dorsal and anal fins. Halfmoons are common in Southern California. Divers most often see them midway between the surface and the bottom in kelp beds.

Reported from the Klamath River, California to the Gulf of California.

57. OPALEYE

58. HALFMOON

59. ZEBRAPERCH   *Hermosilla azurea*
(*) (sky-blue)

Occasionally observed around Southern California kelp beds and over sandy and rock bottoms from the intertidal zone out to 35 feet. Length to 17.4 inches. Look for 9 or 10 dark vertical bars on sides and bright blue spot on operculum.

Shallow inshore waters from Monterey to Gulf of California. Rare north of Pt. Conception.

*Named for capital city of the State of Sonora, Mexico where the typical species was taken.

FAMILY EMBIOTOCIDAE
Surfperch

Note: This family is endemic to the Eastern Pacific region and contains 20 species, one of which is found in freshwater. All members bear live young. I include here the 9 species most likely to be encountered by divers. The remaining species are found mostly in surf and other areas not frequented by divers.

60. RUBBERLIP   *Rhacochilus toxotes*
SURFPERCH   rag lip; toxotes, named after the genus *Toxotes,* the East Indian Archerfish, because of some obscure resemblance.

Frequents rocky areas and kelp beds from the surface to depths of 150 feet. Maximum length is 18½ inches, which makes it the largest member of the surfperch family. Look for large fleshy lips. The 1st ray in the 2nd dorsal fin is shorter than the 3rd ray. Rubberlip surfperch occur as solitary individuals as well as in schools. Diver observation indicates that they are more abundant than the hook-and-line catch would suggest.

Reported from Russian Gulch State Beach, California to Thurloe Head, Baja California.

59. ZEBRAPERCH

60. RUBBERLIP SURFPERCH

61. PILE SURFPERCH   *Damalichthys vacca*
calf-fish; cow

Occurs around piers, jetties, kelp beds and shallow reefs from surface to 150 feet. Length to 17 2/5 inches. Look for long soft rays in dorsal fin, and dark vertical bar on sides. (Bar fades after death.) This is a common species in the catches of sport fishermen fishing off piers.

Port Wrangell, Alaska to Guadalupe Island.

62. WHITE SURFPERCH   *Phanerodon furcatus*
evident tooth; forked

Surface to 140 feet around piers, reefs and bays. Maximum length is 12 2/5 inches. Look for longest soft ray of dorsal fin to be slightly longer than the longest dorsal fin spine.

Vancouver Island, British Columbia to Point Cabras, Baja California.

61. PILE SURFPERCH

62. WHITE SURFPERCH

63. SHARPNOSE SURFPERCH

Phanerodon atripes
evident tooth; black foot

A deeper water surfperch recorded from surface to 750 feet around reefs, kelp beds and piers. Maximum length is 11½ inches. Look for reddish speckles on scales and black tipped pelvic fins. The sharpnose surfperch undergoes dramatic periodic increases in population size. It was the dominant species in Monterey fish markets during the early 1900's, then declined until the 1960's when the population grew again. Occasionally function as "cleaners" and have been observed removing parasites from molas, blue rockfish and blacksmiths.

Bodega Bay, California to San Benito Islands, Baja California.

64. WALLEYE SURFPERCH

Hyperprosopon argenteum
(above face) (silvery)

Schools or loose aggregations common around piers and kelp beds and over sand and rock bottoms to 60 feet. Length to 12 inches. Look for black-tipped pelvic fins and black edging on tail. Walleye surfperch form an important segment of the catches of sportfishers fishing from piers.

Shallow inshore waters and bays from Vancouver Island, British Columbia to Point San Rosarito, Baja California.

63. SHARPNOSE SURFPERCH

64. WALLEYE SURFPERCH

65. BLACK SURFPERCH *Embiotoca jacksoni*

viviparous; Jackson's, after A. C. Jackson who first discovered this species' viviparity.

In shallow bays and to depths of approximately 130 feet around piers, reefs and kelp beds. Maximum length is 15 2/5 inches. Look for patch of enlarged scales between pectoral fin and pelvic fin, yellow-orange lips, blue and orange in anal fin and dark bars on sides when observed underwater. Divers see black surfperch throughout the year, but hook-and-line fishermen find them most abundant during early spring, particularly in bays.

Fort Bragg, California to Point Abreojos, Baja California.

66. STRIPED SURFPERCH *Embiotoca lateralis*

viviparous; lateral (with reference to its blue stripes).

Common in late winter and early spring in bays around piers and jetties; otherwise, throughout the year around reefs and kelp beds as deep as 55 feet. Maximum length is 15 inches. Look for blue horizontal stripes and 29-33 anal fin soft rays which distinguish the striped from the rainbow (No. 67) surfperch. A popular sportfish for hook-and-line fishermen fishing from piers and jetties in Northern California.

Port Wrangell, Alaska to Point Cabras, Baja California.

65. BLACK SURFPERCH

66. STRIPED SURFPERCH

67. RAINBOW SURFPERCH

Hypsurus caryi
high tail; Cary's after T. G. Cary who discovered this fish.

Frequents shallow water around piers, jetties, reefs and kelp beds. Maximum recorded depth is 130 feet. Maximum length is 12 inches. Look for stripes on sides, 20-24 anal fin soft rays, and an abrupt upward curve in body at anal fin which distinguishes it from the striped surfperch (No. 66). One of the most colorful of the surfperch.

Cape Mendocino, California to Rio Santo Tomas, Baja California.

68. KELP SURFPERCH

Brachyistius frenatus
short dorsal fin; bridled

Occurs in kelp beds from surface to 100 foot depths. Maximum length is 8½ inches. Look for dorsal fin with 13-16 soft rays, brassy orange body color, and projecting lower jaw. This fish is a common resident of Central and Southern California kelp forests. They are "cleaners"—that is, they feed on parasites found on other fish such as the blacksmith, kelp bass, opaleye, garibaldi, walleye surfperch, and other kelp surfperch.

Vancouver Island, British Columbia to Turtle Bay, Baja California.

67. RAINBOW SURFPERCH

68. KELP SURFPERCH

69. SHINER SURFPERCH *Cymatogaster aggregata*
fetus belly; crowded together. The generic name refers to the facts that these fish bear live young. *"Aggregata"* refers to schooling behavior.

Common in bays around piers and jetties, but also occurs over mud bottoms offshore, to depths of approximately 480 feet. Length to 7 inches. Look for 3 vertical yellow bars on sides. Males during breeding season have black striping which tends to cover yellow bars. These small surfperch are very popular with youngsters fishing from piers.

Port Wrangell, Alaska to San Quintin Bay, Baja California.

FAMILY POMACENTRIDAE
Damsel Fish

70. GARIBALDI   *Hypsypops rubicundus*
High below eye; red. The generic name is an anatomical description of the wide space between maxillary and eye.

Frequents shallow water kelp beds and reefs. Maximum reported depth is 95 feet. Maximum length to 14 inches. This most distinctive fish is fully protected in California. It is illegal for sport or commercial fishermen to take garibaldi, the only marine fish to enjoy such protection. They are a delight to divers because of their beauty and the fact that they are easy to approach for observation and photography. Juveniles are particularly colorful because of iridescent blue blotching.

Monterey Bay, California to Magdalena Bay, Baja California.

69. SHINER SURFPERCH

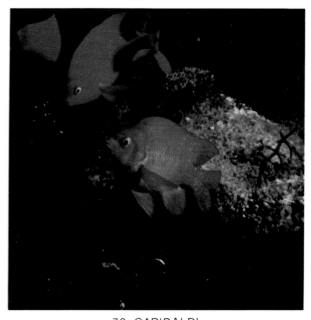

70. GARIBALDI

71. BLACKSMITH   *Chromis punctipinnis*
                        Chromis; spot fin. The genus name is
                        an ancient name for the same fish.

Occurs in kelp beds from the surface to 150 feet. Maximum length
to 12 inches. Look for black spots on dorsal and tail fins. Juveniles
are purple anteriorly and yellow posteriorly. Blacksmith are major
"customers" of the "cleaner" fish which include the senoritas
and the sharpnose surfperch. A swarming type, schooling fish.
They sleep in crevices and on rocks at night.

Monterey, California to Point San Pablo, Baja California.

FAMILY LABRIDAE
Wrasses

72. CALIFORNIA   *Pimelometopon pulchrum*
    SHEEPHEAD   fat forehead; beautiful

Occurs around kelp beds and shallow rocky reefs out to depths of
180 feet. Maximum length to 3 feet and weight to 36¼ pounds.
Look for distinctive black head of male. Both sexes have large
doglike teeth and white chins. Juveniles have 7 black blotches, of
which 5 are visible from the side on fins and the base of the tail.
Sheephead are hermaphroditic; they begin life as females, but after
a few years they change into males for the remainder of their lives.

Monterey to Cape San Lucas, Baja California. There is also an isolated population in the northern Gulf of California.

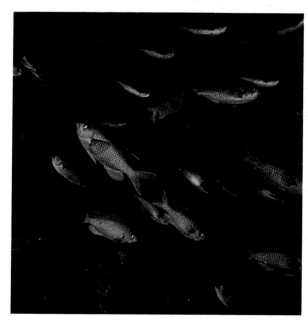

71. BLACKSMITH

Male   Female

72. CALIFORNIA SHEEPHEAD

73. SENORITA

Oxyjulis californica
sharp julis; California. *Julis* is another species of wrasse.

A shallow water fish common around kelp beds and reefs. Maximum recorded depth is 180 feet. Maximum length is 10 inches. Look for black spot on tail fin, large scales, cigar shaped body, dusky orange color, and 13 soft rays in anal fin. This is the most common "cleaner" in our area. Most Southern California divers have observed these fish picking parasites off blacksmiths.

Sausalito, California to Cedros Island, Baja California.

74. ROCK WRASSE

Halichoeres semicinctus
pig-of-the-sea; half-banded

Frequents shallow reefs and kelp beds to depths of approximately 78 feet. Maximum length to 12 9/10 inches. Look for 12 soft rays in anal fin, and abrupt arch in posterior portion of lateral line. Males have a dark blue bar near base of pectoral fin, and red eyes. Rock wrasse are hermaphroditic.

Point Conception, California to the Gulf of California.

73. SENORITA

Male   Female

74. ROCK WRASSE

FAMILY BATHYMASTERIDAE
Ronquils

75. NORTHERN RONQUIL   *Ronquilus jordani*
one who grunts; Jordan's for David Starr Jordan, discoverer of this fish.

Occurs on sand and around shale and rocky reefs in depths from 60 to 540 feet. Maximum length is 7⅛ inches. Look for orange stripes below eye and on lower posterior portion of body. First 20-30 soft rays in dorsal fin are unbranched.

Bering Sea to Monterey Bay.

76. SMOOTH RONQUIL   *Rathbunella hypoplecta*
Rathbun; folded underneath Genus named after U.S. Fish Commissioner, R. Rathbun.

Occurs on sand and reefs intertidally out to at least 100 feet. Maximum length to 8½ inches. Look for pigmented fin rays, greenish blotch on base of pectoral fin, and the first 15 soft rays in dorsal fin unbranched. Unlike northern ronquil (No. 75), smooth has no orange stripes.

Pacific Northwest to Northern Baja California. Common around shale reefs in Monterey Bay and off Point Loma, California.

75. NORTHERN RONQUIL

76. SMOOTH RONQUIL

FAMILY ANARHICHADIDAE
Wolf Fish

77. WOLF-EEL *Anarrhichthys ocellatus*
anarhichas fish; eye-like spot

Occurs in rocky areas in crevices and caves; sometimes ventures over sand, intertidally to 400 feet. Maximum recorded length is 6⅔ feet; reports of 8 foot specimens extremely doubtful. Preys on market crabs (*Cancer magister*) and other crustaceans. Capable of inflicting serious injury but harmless unless provoked.

Sea of Japan and Kodiak Island, Alaska to Imperial Beach, San Diego County, California.

FAMILY CLINIDAE
Kelp Fish

Note: 12 species of this family occur in our area. Most are small and use protective coloration or hide in holes and crevices. We describe here 5 species that divers commonly encounter.

78. ONESPOT *Neoclinus uninotatus*
FRINGEHEAD new clinid; one-marked (in reference to the single ocellus on the dorsal fin).

Occurs in crevices, holes, old cans and bottles on sandy and mud bottoms, and around reefs in depths from 10 to 90 feet. Maximum lengths to 9 inches. Look for large cirrus above eye—that is, cirrus is longer than diameter of eye. Also, there is a single ocellus in anterior dorsal fin, and a maxillary that extends well beyond back of eye. Usually, divers see only the head of these fish protruding from their hiding place.

Bodega Bay to San Diego Bay, California.

77. WOLF-EEL

78. ONESPOT FRINGEHEAD

79. SARCASTIC FRINGEHEAD

Neoclinus blanchardi
new clinid; Blanchard's, after S. B. Blanchard, discoverer of this fish.

Same habitat and behavior as onespot fringehead (No.78) but has been recorded at depths to 200 feet. Length to 12 inches. Look for 2 ocelli in dorsal fin, 1 between 1st and 2nd spine, the other between the 5th and 9th spines, and a maxillary extending almost to the back edge of the gill cover. The maxillary is larger in the mature male than in the female.

San Francisco to Cedros Island, Baja California.

80. ISLAND KELPFISH

Alloclinus holderi
different clinid; Holder's, after naturalist C. H. Holder

Frequents rocky areas from the intertidal zone to 162 feet. Maximum length to 4 inches. Look for pectoral fin extending at least to origin of anal fin, maxillary reaching beyond middle of eye, and an abruptly descending lateral line about mid-body.

Santa Cruz Island, California to Point San Pablo, Baja California. Common around Santa Catalina Island.

79. SARCASTIC FRINGEHEAD

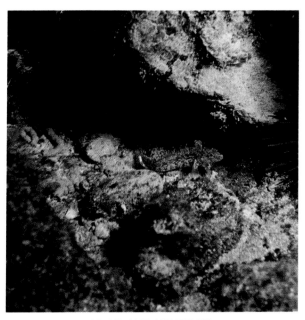

80. ISLAND KELPFISH

81. GIANT KELPFISH   *Heterostichus rostratus*
different ranks; long-nosed

Frequents kelp beds intertidally to 132 feet, usually in close association with the kelp plants. Maximum length to 24 inches. Look for forked tail and 31-35 soft rays in anal fin. Color varies greatly but usually closely matches the particular kelp in the vicinity.

British Columbia to Cape San Lucas, Baja California.

82. CREVICE KELPFISH   *Gibbonsia montereyensis*
Gibbons; Monterey. W. P. Gibbons was an early naturalist with the California Academy of Sciences.

Found intertidally to 25 feet around rocks and kelp. Maximum length to 4.44 inches. Look for 2 or more dark spots on sides. Posterior portion of caudal peduncle lacks scales. There are 4 members of the genus *Gibbonsia* in our area, and they are extremely difficult to tell apart, even out of the water. However, just 2 species occur north of Monterey. The other one is the striped kelpfish (*Gibbonsia metzi*) which lacks the spots on the sides. Instead it has 1 or 2 lateral stripes, and evenly spaced dorsal soft rays.

British Columbia to Rio Santo Tomas, Baja California.

81. GIANT KELPFISH

82. CREVICE KELPFISH

FAMILY CEBIDICHTHYIDAE

83. MONKEYFACE-EEL   *Cebidichthys violaceus*
(monkey fish) (violet)

Occurs around rocky areas intertidally out to 80 feet. Most common in rocky intertidal zone. Length to 30 inches. Look for humps on top of head, single lateral line and dark bars below eye. A very specialized sport fishery has evolved for this fish called "poke poling". Fishermen use long cane poles with a piece of 6 to 10 inch monofilament which has a small hook attached to the end. The baited hook is poked between intertidal rocks and into crevices and holes, where monkey-face eels are most abundant, during low tides.

Crescent City, California to San Quintin Bay, Baja California.

FAMILY GOBIIDAE
Gobies

Note: 14 species of gobies occur in our area, but only 3 are commonly encountered by divers. All gobies have pelvic fins that are joined together to form a cone which they use to adhere to objects. This family also includes the smallest known fish, a tropical species that in adulthood is less than ½ inch long.

84. BLACKEYE GOBY   *Coryphopterus nicholsii*
head fin; Nichols'. The genus name refers to a fleshy crest on head. Species named after Captain H. E. Nichols, U.S.N., discoverer of this fish.

Frequents intertidal rocky and sandy bottoms to 80 feet. Maximum length to 6 inches. Look for iridescent blue spot beneath eye, pelvic and pectoral fins that reach vent, (Anus) and a black area on outer edge of first dorsal fin. Blackeye gobies are very common and most divers are familier with them. However, they are rarely taken by hook-and-line fishermen.

Queen Charlotte Island, British Columbia to Point Rompiente, Baja California.

83. MONKEYFACE-EEL

84. BLACKEYE GOBY

85. BLUEBANDED GOBY *Lythrypnus dalli*

red sleeper; Dali's, after W. H. Dall, discoverer of this fish.

Occurs intertidally out to 210 feet around rocks. Maximum length to 2¼ inches. Look for a bright red fish with 2-6 bright blue vertical bands on body and 12-14 anal fin soft rays. Bluebanded goby is one of the most colorful fishes divers encounter in our area.

Reported from Morro Bay, California to the Gulf of California. Very common around Santa Catalina Island.

86. ZEBRA GOBY *Lythrypnus zebra*

red sleeper; zebra

Occurs in same habitat as bluebanded goby, except that maximum recorded depth is 318 feet. Maximum length is also 2¼ inches. Similar to bluebanded, but body is more of an orange-red, there are 12-16 vertical blue bands, and only 9 soft rays in anal fin. Zebra gobies are less often seen than bluebanded gobies.

Lion Rock, San Luis Obispo County, California to Guadalupe Island.

85. BLUEBANDED GOBY

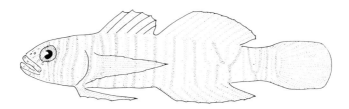

86. ZEBRA GOBY

FAMILY BOTHIDAE
Lefteye Flounders

Note: Both the eye and body colors of these flounders tend to be on the left side of the body. There are 6 species in our area, but we show photographs of only two of the more common and sought after species.

87. CALIFORNIA HALIBUT

Paralichthys californicus
parallel fish; California

Occurs from surf zone to depths of 300 feet on sand and mud bottoms. Maximum length to 5 feet and weight to 72 pounds. Look for large mouth filled with strong sharp teeth, and a high arch in the lateral line above the pectoral fin. A fine food fish much sought-after by divers, hook-and-line fishermen, and commercial net fishermen. Almost half the time, the eyes and the coloration will be on the right rather than the left side of the body.

Quillayute River, British Columbia to Magdalena Bay, Baja California.

88. PACIFIC SANDDAB

Citharichthys sordidus
rib fish; sordid. "Sordid" is used here in the sense of dull color.

Occurs on sand and mud bottoms in depths from 30 to 1800 feet. Length to 16 inches. Look for snout that is longer than diameter of lower eye, and pectoral fin that would reach mid-eye if projected forward. Small pacific sanddabs (those under 6 inches) are almost impossible to distinguish from the speckled sanddab (*C. stigmaeus*) when viewed underwater. A very tasty flatfish.

Bering Sea to Cape San Lucas, Baja California.

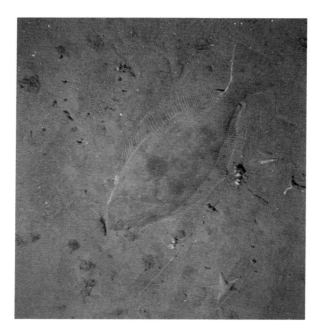

87. CALIFORNIA HALIBUT

88. PACIFIC SANDDAB

FAMILY PLEURONECTIDAE
Righteye Flounders

Note: 22 species of righteye flounders are found in our area. Some are of tremendous commercial importance, but only a few are ever seen by divers. We show here photographs of the 4 species that are most commonly encountered by skin and SCUBA divers.

89. ROCK SOLE *Lepidopsetta bilineata*
(Scale flounder) (two-lined)

Common particularly in Southeastern Alaska on sand, mud and rock bottoms from 10 to 480 feet. Maximum recorded size is 22.5 inches. Look for the dorsal branch of the lateral line that extends towards tail and rough scales. The color is highly variable and depends on the type of bottom on which the fish is resting.

Bering Sea and Sea of Japan south to Tanner Bank.

90. STARRY FLOUNDER *Platichthys stellatus*
flat fish; starry

Occurs in shallow bays and on sand and mud bottoms to depths of 900 feet. Maximum length to 3 feet and weight to 20 pounds. Look for dark bars on dorsal, anal and tail fins, and scattered rough scales on side with eyes. Although classified as a righteyed flounder, the eyes and coloration also occur commonly on the left side.

Sea of Japan and Arctic Alaska to Santa Barbara, California.

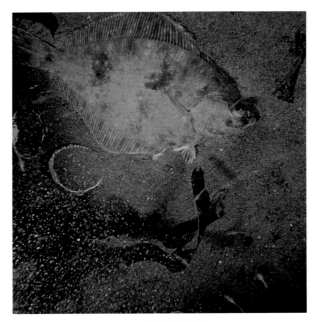

89. ROCK SOLE

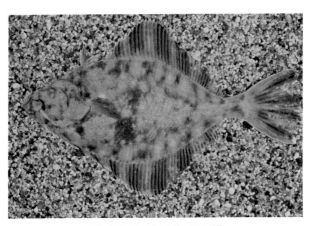

90. STARRY FLOUNDER

91. C-O TURBOT *Pleuronichthys coenosus*
side fish; muddy

Occurs on sand and around reefs from shallow water to 210 feet. Length to 14 inches. Look for location of 1st 5 or 6 dorsal fin rays on blind side, and the following tail markings: anterior mark in the form of a half-moon, posterior mark in form of large round dark blotch. Also, there is a dark spot in middle of body.

Southeastern Alaska to Cape Colnett, Baja California.

92. DIAMOND TURBOT *Hypsopsetta guttulata*
deep flounder; with small spots

Frequents sand and mud bottoms in bays as well as shallow coastal waters to depths of 150 feet. Maximum length to 18 inches. Look for light blue spotting on body and porcelain white underside with some lemon yellow coloring near the mouth and margin of the head. This is the only flatfish so colored.

Cape Mendocino to Magdalena Bay, Baja California.

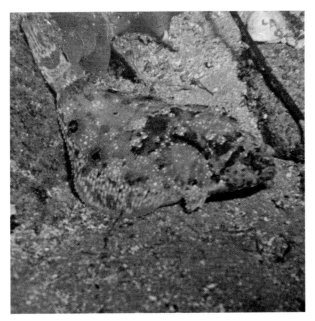

91. C-O TURBOT

92. DIAMOND TURBOT

FAMILY MOLIDAE
Molas

Note: Molas occur throughout the world in warm and temperate seas, some reaching tremendous size. There are two in our area, and we have photographed one of them.

93. COMMON MOLA   *Mola mola*
millstone; millstone

A pelagic wanderer usually observed on or near the surface. Maximum reported length to 13.1 feet, weight to 3300 pounds, but both are probably exaggerated estimates. Molas are common along the coast during the late summer and fall. An unusual die-off occurs for unknown reasons in Monterey Bay during the fall season. Molas have been observed being cleaned by sharpnose surfperch, rainbow surfperch, and senoritas. They often jump clear of the water and flip over while in the air. Molas can move rapidly when startled. Considered desirable as food by some.

Found all along Pacific coast north to British Columbia.

93. COMMON MOLA

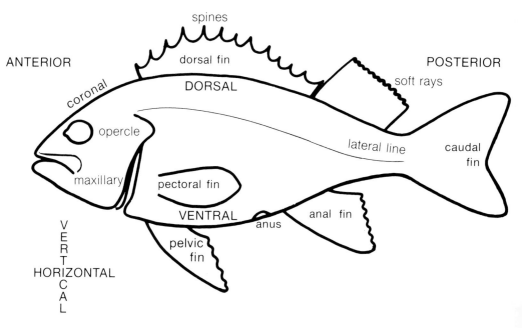

Figure A. Terms used to indicate place or direction.

anal —near the anus
anterior—near the head
caudal —near the origin of
the tail
coronal—near the top of the
head
dorsal —on or near the back;
in fish, along the top
edge

pectoral —near pectoral fin,
see chart
pelvic —see chart
posterior—near the tail, the
rear of the fish
ventral —on or near the belly;
the bottom of the fish.

INDEX TO COMMON NAMES

BIBLIOGRAPHY

Baxter, John L., *Inshore Fishes of California.* 3rd Rev. Ed., California Department of Fish and Game, Sacramento, 1960.

Fitch, John E., *Offshore Fishes of California.* 4th Rev. Ed., California Department of Fish and Game, Sacramento, 1969.

Fitch, John E. and Robert J. Lavenberg, *Deep-water Teleostean Fishes of California,* University of California Press, Berkeley, 1968.
_____, *Marine Food and Game Fishes of California.* University of California Press, Berkeley, 1971.

Hart, J.L., *Pacific Fishes of Canada.* Fish. Research Board of Canada, Bulletin (180): 1-740, 1973.

Herald, Earl S. *Living Fishes of the World.* Doubleday and Co., New York, 1961.
_____ *Fishes of North America.* Doubleday and Co., New York, 1972.

Miller, Daniel J. and Robert N. Lea, *Guide to the Coastal Marine Fishes of California,* California Department of Fish and Game, Bulletin (157): 1-235, Sacramento, 1972.

FISH IDENTIFIED

_____

_____

_____

_____

_____

_____

_____

_____

_____

_____

_____

_____

_____

_____

_____

_____

_____

_____

_____

_____

_____

_____

_____

_____

_____

_____

FISH IDENTIFIED